Mathematics for
Young Children

What, Why, and How

by
Jean M. Shaw, Ed. D.

Table of Contents

Introduction

With increasing pressure for educational achievement and accompanying legislation such as No Child Left Behind, early childhood educators are aware of the need to study, evaluate, and upgrade the mathematics experiences they offer to three- to six-year old children. Young children's curiosity about the world, their capacity for investigating and learning mathematics, and the role that mathematics plays in the child's world all help to make a strong case for a broad, engaging math, developmentally-appropriate curriculum (Neil, 2001).

Not only should early childhood educators consider exposing children to a broad range of content in mathematics, they should be aware of the role that mathematics processes such as problem solving, communication, and representation play. When content and process are blended together, children begin to gain a full view of what mathematics is and how it is used.

The purpose of this short book is to provide teachers and caregivers of three-to six-year old children some background in teaching math to young children. Chapter 1 provides information about the nature and need for good mathematics for young children. Chapters 2-6 include NCTM content areas: numbers and operations, algebra, geometry, measurement, and data analysis and probability. Each of these chapters offers a brief description of content, activities for enhancing learning, related children's books, and summary of the importance of pre-first grade content to primary and elementary grades. Inherent in each of these chapters is attention to math processes such as communication and problem solving. A final section includes references.

Intended to be brief, readable, and practical, this book may be a starting place and stimulus for study and development of existing programs and classroom activities. Teachers, caregivers, program directors, parents, and others will want to adapt and expand its contents to meet the needs of individuals and groups of children as well as to increase the quality of learning opportunities they offer to children.

Chapter 1

Mathematics for Young Children: What, Why, and How

Young children are typically eager to learn more about the world around them. Because they like to compare quantities, make designs, move about in our three-dimensional world, explore relationships, and describe shapes, sizes, and numbers, preschool children are wonderful, natural mathematicians.

What is appropriate mathematics content for young children?

The National Council of Teachers of Mathematics (NCTM) has been extremely influential in advocating for more and better mathematics for all students. NCTM's Curriculum and Evaluation Standards for School Mathematics (1989) and Principles and Standards for School Mathematics (2000) have impacted curriculum and teacher training in virtually every state. Educators in most states have developed their guidelines for kindergarten and pre-kindergarten mathematics based on these NCTM standards. NCTM's (2000) recommendations for pre-K through second grade mathematics provide the basis for this book.

NCTM (2000) advocates five **content** areas for pre-K through 12th grade students. These are:

- **number and operations** (Adding and subtracting are of most interest for three-to six-year olds).
- **algebra**.
- **geometry**.
- **measurement**.
- **data analysis and probability**.

Work with these interrelated areas gives young children a solid and effective foundation for the mathematics they will use the rest of their lives.

Also important are mathematics **processes** – things people do as they learn and use mathematics. NCTM (2000) describes five processes that are used all through mathematics.

Problem solving

Problem solving requires application of knowledge and higher-level thinking and draws upon attitudes of curiosity and persistence.

Reasoning and proof

Mathematics should make sense. Reasoning and proof are fundamental aspects of math, and children engage in them as they explain their answers and thinking processes.

Communication

Communication is a vital area for young children. Through words, gestures, body language, listening, writing and drawing, and reading, they share ideas with others and use and refine pertinent vocabulary.

Representation

Closely related to communication, representation is using and creating images and symbols to organize, record, and communicate mathematical ideas.

Connections

Connections means relating content areas of mathematics and linking math to the real world and to other subject matter areas.

For each content area, all of the process area can be used.

For example, as children work with triangles, they might first connect to the real world by finding examples of triangles in the classroom and making drawings to represent triangles. (Figure 1.2) Then they might solve the problem of finding out how many ways they can combine two triangles to make other figures. After children work with pairs of paper triangles, they might show their results, using their arrangements as a stimulus for communication.

Content (what we study) and **process** (how we study and work with it) interrelate and combine to form a strong framework or fabric for planning mathematics experiences for young children. It may be pictured as shown. (Figure 1.1)

	Problem Solving	Reasoning & Proof	Communication	Connections	Representation
Number & Operations					
Algebra					
Geometry					
Measurement					
Data Analysis & Probability					

Figure 1.1 - "A Fabric of Mathematics"

7

They use reasoning as a child explains how he flipped one triangle over, then combined it with another to produce the first figure shown. When asked whether the second and third arrangements are different, a child might turn one arrangement around to show how the two are alike.

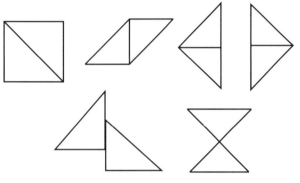

Figure 1.2

Why do young children need informal and formal experiences with mathematics?

Authors of *Adding It Up* (2001), and *Eager To Learn* (2000) state that young children show mathematical competence; indeed authors of *Eager To Learn* assert that children know "more in the preschool years than was previously understood" (p. 7). "At no other time in schooling is cognitive growth so remarkable" (NCTM, 2000). Copley (2000) asserts that children have a natural enthusiasm for mathematics. All children can learn; all should

have access to good mathematics in a positive and supportive environment. Children need direct teaching about mathematics as well as child-centered, hands-on activities and discussion of those activities. Teachers and caregivers should also take advantage of "teachable moments" that arise during the day: weighing a pet that visits the classroom, counting to see which drinks are preferred for snack time, using math-oriented songs and fingerplays, using art papers of various shapes and sizes, and providing a calculator for use in the classroom store and home living center.

Understanding of mathematics is necessary for everyday tasks such as spending and saving money, pursuing hobbies, voting intelligently, and finding jobs in today's technological world. People with strong math backgrounds have wider choices of future schooling and professions. Mathematics is also a part of human achievement and cultural heritage; understanding and appreciating it is vital (NCTM, 2000).

American educators are challenged to improve learning opportunities for all students. International competition, the need for well-prepared workers, and increasing technology all support the idea that more and better mathematics is needed for our children.

How can teachers and caregivers enhance children's learning of mathematics?

The following ideas may guide educators in thinking about quality math programs for young children.

Use knowledge of children and how they learn. Learning about children's interests and needs will suggest to teachers and caregivers ways to motivate and reinforce children's efforts. Careful observation as well as conversations with family members can reveal much about things that children like to do and things they need help with. Most young children are active, concrete learners. They must use and develop both their large and small muscles. Math activities that involve movement, attractive manipulative materials, and open-ended outcomes appeal to children and help them learn.

Engage children in multisensory experiences. When several senses are involved, young children's learning is enhanced. Adults can consider potential learning activities and be sure that children use several senses. Instead of merely offering verbal directions, a teacher may show an example (something to see), then have several children participate in demonstrating and telling what to do. For example, the teacher may introduce the number 5 showing five fingers, clapping 5 times, and writing the numeral. She may engage children in showing five in a variety of ways including gently tracing or "writing" on the backs of their hands. Preparing a recipe is another wonderful way for children to compare, count, and measure as well as helping to read numbers, discussing what they are doing, touching and smelling small samples of ingredients, and tasting the results!

Provide manipulative materials. Gather materials for children to use at math time and at free choice times during the day. Large buttons, colored connecting cubes, and wooden beads can be used for sorting, counting, and creating geometric shapes. Small plastic figures such as teddy bear counters inspire counting, comparing sets, and telling number stories. Tiles or counters with different colors or textures on each side can be used for counting, representing and comparing numbers, and generating data. (Figure 1.3) A variety of boxes and cans might be sorted or identified as geometric shapes. Pattern blocks let children sort, combine and subdivide figures, and create patterns and symmetrical shapes. Andrews (2004) suggests attaching self-adhesive magnet strips to the backs of pattern blocks for display on magnet board – or on a steel cookie sheet. Balance scales let children compare weights. Real and plastic money invites sorting, counting, trading, and dramatic play. Homemade or purchased spinners can be used in probability experiments to generate numbers for games.

Promote literacy and vocabulary as children learn math. Educators have important responsibilities for children's language growth as well as mathematical development. Language is a vital component of mathematics. Children must talk about mathematical ideas as well as listen. They can also draw and demonstrate to show their understanding. Even five-year-olds can begin to keep math journals in which they draw examples of important ideas (larger and smaller, 5 objects, circles and triangles). A wide variety of math-oriented books adds much to the classroom library. Math ideas are also inherent in many stories, and adults can use literature as a meaningful and appealing springboard to mathematics. Clements and Samara (2004) suggest reading stories in their entirety, then asking open-ended questions and rereading parts to pursue their mathematical ideas.

Be aware of opportunities for math learning throughout the day. Math is much more than something for children to do in the math center or a lesson at 9:30 each day. Math ideas can be used throughout the entire day. For example, as children enter the classroom, they might move a marker or name card to make a graph-like arrangement when they arrive. As a routine, the teacher might lead counting of the number of boys and girls present; children can compare the day's total to yesterday's. Children can use counting and one-to-one correspondence as they help to set up napkins and snack foods. They might use a timer to see how much they can clean up in a given interval. The class might count and compare numbers of "giant steps" and baby steps as they move from one location to another. Children's attention can be drawn to the order of activities throughout the day and times on the clock. They can use counting, pictures, and tallies to record how many birds and squirrels come to a feeder over a period of days. As children line up, caregivers can use ordinal numbers to call out who can be first, second, third, and so on; they might then establish that "first" is number 1 in line (Clements and Samara, 2004) Of course many other applications are possible!

Teach for understanding. "Students must learn mathematics with understanding, actively building new knowledge from experience and prior knowledge" (NCTM, 2000, p. 20). Many benefits accrue from understanding. When children understand content, as opposed to simply memorizing it, they feel confident. They can apply content in new situations more readily and learn skills more easily. Understanding may be enhanced by actively engaging children in learning, letting them express and test ideas, and talk about what they are doing. Most preschool children already have prior knowledge of some mathematics. Discussing what they already know – as well as finding out what misconceptions they may have – recognizes competencies, relates math to real experience, and helps teachers and caregivers planning ways to extend children's learning.

Provide opportunities for children to use math processes. The processes of problem solving, reasoning, communicating, connecting, and representing are important parts of mathematics. Problem solving will be enhanced if teachers and caregivers pose open-ended questions and give children chances to figure out solutions. Though it may be faster and easier for adults to provide solutions, most children will not become independent problem solvers without practice. Reasoning, communication, and representation are used by asking children to explain their answers. Explaining should be expected whether children offer right or wrong answers; children may explain verbally or show ideas and solutions with manipulatives. They can also be encouraged to listen carefully to each other's responses, then paraphrase or respond to classmates.

Use appropriate assessment. Assessment should enhance children's learning. Teachers and caregivers, through careful observation and documentation of children's learning and problems with learning, can make decisions of how to help each child progress. To make decisions effectively, adults should use data from many sources – from products and samples of written work, discussions and responses to questions, interviews, and children's self-assessments. A single day's performance or single task shows only a small sample of any child's abilities (Shaw and Blake, 1998). Test results for young children are highly unreliable and must be used with caution when making decisions about children's strengths and weaknesses.

Collaborate and learn! "Effective teaching requires continually seeking improvement" (NCTM, 2000, p. 19). Observing children, listening carefully to their responses and requests, sharing ideas and problems with others helps educators grow professionally. Participating in professional development and workshop opportunities, and reading are other important ways to gain information that will help teachers and caregivers improve their understanding of mathematics and ways it can be effectively taught to young children.

Chapter 2

Number and Operations

As kindergarten children review the books they have read in the past month, Jack shouts, "That one was my favorite!" Ms. Abby thanks him, then has all the children designate a favorite as she records their choices. Next she leads the children in counting the number of children who chose each book. When she asks, "Which book was the favorite of more of us? How can we find out?" the children suggest various ways to determine the answer.

Number and Operations for Young Children

When asked to describe mathematics, the first thing most people mention is working with numbers. Indeed numbers are an important part of math; they help people describe quantitative aspects of the world. As long as people have kept records – of time, events, and possessions – they have used numbers. Virtually every society and culture has devised a number system.

Authors of *Adding It Up* (2001) assert that number is at the "heart of preschool, elementary, and middle school mathematics" (p. 20). Indeed math for three- to six-year olds includes counting, recognition and representation of numbers, comparing quantities, exploring fractions, and conceptualizing and modeling addition and subtraction. Numbers and operations also have a natural part in other math content areas: algebraic thinking, geometry, measurement, and data analysis. (NCTM, 2000)

Active learning and understanding – not just pencil and paper and rote memorization – contribute to children's development of numbers. Children must explore the meanings of numbers and ways to represent and compare them (3 is greater than 2; 6 is double 3; 5 is less than 10; 5 can be broken or decomposed as 2 and 3) (Esposito and Ness, 2003). They should connect number words and symbols to the quantities they represent and use varied models and materials to express whole numbers and commonly-used fractions such as $\frac{1}{2}$, $\frac{1}{3}$, and $\frac{1}{4}$. "Counting is the foundation for young children's early work with numbers" (NCTM, 2000, p. 79). Though counting is automatic for adults, children must learn number names in an accurate sequence ("one, two, three, four,..."). They must count each object once (the order of counting does not matter as long as each is accounted for). For efficient and accurate counting, children also must realize that arrangement of objects (Piaget's conservation idea) does not affect the number; the last number named tells how many objects are in a set. As part of their exploration of the world, children are motivated to count. They learn to associate number names with small collections of objects and may move or point to objects in sets with greater numbers as they count them. Children also use counting as they develop addition and subtraction strategies.

Young children must also begin to understand the various meanings of addition and subtraction. Addition may mean combining objects or it may involve finding out how many are in two or more sets, even though the sets are not combined. Subtraction may mean a "take away" situation such as spending money, people leaving, or giving away or using up objects. Subtraction is also used to compare sets or find a difference – telling how many more are in one set than another – and to find missing parts. To set the stage for computational fluency that is expected for addition and subtraction in the primary grades, three- to six-year old children can begin to develop and use strategies for adding and subtracting with whole numbers.

Activities for Learning about Number and Operations

Use activities such as these to help children explore number and operations. Materials needed for activities are shown in bold type.

Everyday Counts!
Counting is an important skill; short periods of practice each day help children become comfortable with it. Make counting a meaningful activity by counting the number of children who are present, the number who have returned forms, the number wearing jackets, numbers of crackers or celery sticks for snacks, and so on. Let children count the number of chairs at a table and arrange that many papers or crayons for the occupants. Keep track of numbers that recur such as numbers of boys and girls who come to school to model writing numerals and comparing numbers from day to day.

Once children are familiar with counting to a number such as 20, help them practice counting by twos. You might pair children, then help them count themselves saying the first number for each pair very softly and the second number more loudly: 1, **2**, 3, **4**, 5, **6**, 7, **8**,... Also help children count beyond that number. Lead counting of part of a set, pause and restate the number, then count on more objects (1, 2, 3, 4, 5, 6. 6 pennies in the jar. 7, 8, 9, 10.) (Figure 2.1) Say numbers and help children practice counting on 1 or 2, and counting back 1 or 2.

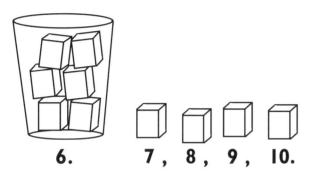

Figure 2.1

Counting Days of School
Because of its versatility and opportunities for developing number sense, counting at least 100 days of school is a meaningful activity for young children. It takes just a few minutes and lets children revisit the counting process daily. It takes several months before the hundredth day is reached, and children who were not ready early in the school year to make sense of the process can "grow into" it as the year progresses.

Teachers or caregivers can announce, write, and display the number of that day of school, then lead the group in counting previous numbers. If the number for every other day is written in a different color, a pattern emerges, and teachers can lead counting by twos. Since numbers are used in

both their ordinal and cardinal sense (the seventh day of school uses the number 7), children regularly experience the use of numbers. A penny or counting cube might be added to a jar for each school day. For five- or six-year olds, as 5 pennies are available, these can be traded for nickels, and each 2 nickels for a dime.

Celebrate 100 Days
Before the hundredth day of school, read a book about the event. You might assign "homework" for each family-creating a display of 100 small items (pieces of cereal, toothpicks, old puzzle pieces, paper clips). On the 100th day, re-read a book, let children show their displays, and have a snack that involves 100 for the class (carrot sticks, pretzels, marshmallows to top cupcakes, or small crackers). You might help children count items by hundreds from their displays (100, 200, 300, ...). Lead other activities such as having children guess how far 100 steps will be from the classroom door and walking off the distance, recounting coins or cubes from the 100 days, or working a group to make 100 clay balls.

One-to-One
One-to-one correspondence lets children compare numbers. Have three children stand and let others decide how many chairs are needed for them. Have the children sit on

the chairs to be sure there is a chair for each and none left over. Display 4 cups and let children match a plate for each. Show 5 books and let children match them one-to-one with "readers." Show children how to line up set objects to see if there is one-to-one correspondence. If so, the numbers are the same. If not, one number is more and the other is less.

Find Your Table
After children wash their hands for snack time, each can be given a card with 1-6 dots on it. Children then match the cards to find their tables. (Dobbs, Doctoroff, and Fisher, 2003) Once children can easily do this, they might match numerals – or geometric shapes.

A Color Graph
Children can use one-to-one correspondence as well as counting to interpret a graph. Offer **small squares of paper** in two colors to about half the class, asking each to choose a favorite color. Have the children line up holding their colors as the others sort them into two groups. Invite children to sit with their colored papers, matching up the children as far as possible. Ask questions such as "Which group has more? Which has fewer or are they the same? How can we tell?" Lead counting of the number in each group. You might let children tape their papers to a bulletin board in a graph-like

arrangement and record children's comments about the display. Repeat the process with the other half of the class choosing colors.

Introducing Numbers
After experiences with counting aloud and informal exposure to numbers, begin representing them with objects. Children can use **cards with pictures** to place a counter on each image. Encourage counting aloud as counters are arranged. Include several different arrangements for each number.

How Many Ways Can We Show It?
Representing numbers many ways helps children understand that the same number can apply to many different situations. Choose a number such as 5 and show it several ways – with 5 claps, one finger on one hand and four on the other, 2 green blocks and 3 yellow ones, and with five books. Challenge children to demonstrate many other ways of representing the number – with objects, gestures, and drawings. Have children share their ideas.

Number Puzzles
As children use number puzzles independently, they build associations between numerals and sets of objects. Prepare **puzzle-like pieces** with numerals and sets of objects. (Figure 2.2) Children may place counters on one puzzle piece

or simply use the images provided. Some six-year olds may be ready for puzzles with a third part which shows a number word.

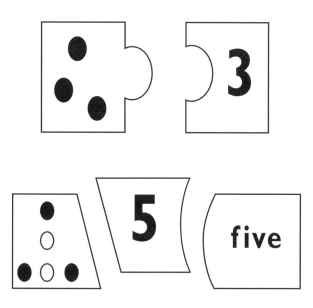

Figure 2.2

Number Dot Cards
Objects that represent numbers may be arranged many different ways; this activity lets children work with some of them. Prepare **small cards** that show several different configurations for each number 1-10 or higher. You might want to write the numeral on the back of each card. Have children sort the cards by number.

Children can work in pairs to compare number cards. With a "more and less" spinner, they might compare pairs of cards. The player whose card matches the spinner takes both cards. If the numbers are the same, they can be shuffled into the pile. Another way to play is one player spinning the spinner and the partner chooses one of his cards to match the spinner. Children can also show cards to partners who say the number, or say a number one more or less than the number shown.

Number Booklets
Using many different materials helps children sustain interest in making a number book. Have children make one or two pages each day for a book to show numbers 0-10 or 0-12. Offer materials such as **markers, stickers, hole punchers, stamps and stamp pad, small pieces of paper and glue, or paint and small brushes**. Provide models of numerals and encourage children to write a numeral on each page. When pages are complete, help children staple them together. (Figure 2.3)

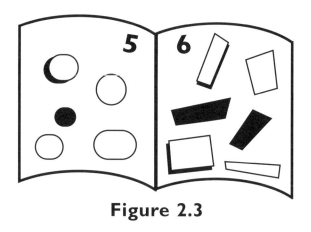

Figure 2.3

Zero? Zero!
A special number is needed to show "none" or "not any." Lead children in counting various objects in the

room – desks, rugs, file cabinets, windows and so on. Record numbers of each. Now ask for objects that are not in the room. "How many sofas do we have? How many swing sets in the room?" If children do not know the number 0, introduce it and show children how it is written. Let children name other things of which there are zero in the classroom.

Picturing 10

Ten is a vital number in our base-ten numeration system; the ten-frame helps children picture it and its relationships to other numbers. Make **ten-frame mats** using a five and five arrangement that mirrors our five fingers on each hand. (Figure 2.4) Teach children to fill the ten frame starting at the upper left and completing the top row first. Call out various numbers for children to arrange on the ten frame, then tell whether it is filled or not. Point out that a number such as 14 is ten and 4 more. For numbers less than 10, let children tell how many more would be needed to reach to 10.

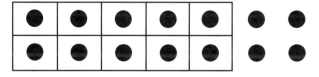

14 is 10 and 4 more.

Figure 2.4

Estimating

Children are ready to estimate once they have well-developed ideas of more, less, and 10. An estimation is a quick but reasoned guess. As you show items for estimating, do not display them long enough for children to count. Begin by showing 10 small items – pennies, candies, cubes – for children to use as a referent. Show another number of the same items, perhaps 6 or 15. Invite children to offer estimates of about how many objects there are. Record their estimates. Let children tell why or how they made their estimates. Finally have children count the number of objects. Estimating should be quick and easy. Do it two or three times a week.

Using a Number Line

A number line displays numerals in order and it's fun for four-to six-year old children to walk along it as they count and discuss numbers. After children have some familiarity with numbers to 10, distribute large number cards, 0-5 or 0-10. Let classmates tell the cardholders how they should stand to be in order, least to greatest. Once they are arranged, lead the class in counting as children hold up their number cards. Have the class close their eyes as one or two children with number cards turn them around. Let the class tell the "missing" numbers.

Lay the number cards in order on the floor and play games such as these. Children can take turns walking to designated numbers as the class counts. A child can stand on a designated number as the class predicts where she will be by taking 3 steps forward or 2 steps back. Two children can stand on numbers as the class identifies which one is on the greater number or identifies what numbers are between them. Have children tell who is standing on 8 or who is on numbers less than 4. Invite children to suggest other tasks.

More Ideas for Number Lines
You might make a number line on a piece of vinyl shelf paper and place it in a location where children line up. Encourage children to say the numbers as they walk on them. Ask questions such as: "What numbers are between Amy and Carlos? Who's on numbers less than Jorge's number?"

As children are exposed to numbers greater than 10, extend the number line to represent the number of teeth lost by children over the year, for example. Copley (2000) suggests writing both numbers and tallies on a strip of paper. As numbers build beyond 10, the strip may be cut and its pieces arranged together to form a partial hundreds chart.

Sand Writing – and More
Engage children's senses and minds with experiences in writing numerals. Print number cards on

pieces of manila folder or tag board. You may want to include number dot patterns as well. Lay a number card in a shallow pan; cover it with a thin layer of sand or cornmeal so the number is partly visible. Encourage children to use a finger to trace around the numeral. (Figure 2.5)

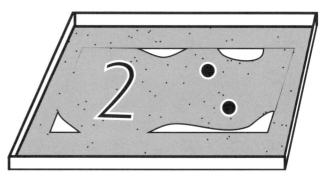

Figure 2.5

Use other sensory materials such as small amounts of shaving cream or fingerpaint on the tabletop. Let children write numerals on the sidewalk with plain water and small paintbrushes or form numerals of playdough.

Writing number symbols is an important way of representing quantities. As with writing letters, it takes practice over time. Provide number models and a variety of kinds and sizes of paper. Even easel paper and paint makes a good medium for writing. Encourage numeral writing as part of other activities on "lists" in the classroom store or housekeeping area, to keep track of blocks used in a construction, or for interested children to write numbers of the days of school.

Fractions
Use children's familiarity with sharing as you work with fractions. Help them fold and cut **paper squares and circles** to make two equal parts – each part is one half. Offer **play dough or clay** to form into "pies, "pizzas" or "cakes" to share. Let children share sets of objects too. For example, if two children share 8 blocks, each gets half the blocks or 4 blocks. Encourage children to cut paper or dough shapes in half, then half again to form fourths.

Understanding Addition and Subtraction
Telling and acting out stories helps children understand what operations mean. Have each child draw a **picture of a pond and island**. Let children use **counters** to act out stories such as this one: "One turtle was swimming in the pond. One turtle was on the island. How many turtles in all? How can we find out? " Invite several explanations or demonstrations. Help children find other sums or totals, using key phrases such as "in all," "total," and "altogether." In a like manner, illustrate subtraction situations such as these: "Four birds were wading in the water. One turtle was in the water. How many more birds than turtles?" "Six turtles were sunning themselves.

Two went swimming. How many turtles were left in the sun?" Let children create and share stories for classmates to solve. Make the materials available for more informal storytelling.

Earning, Spending, and Saving
Coins make a realistic prop for working with addition and subtraction. Provide coins such as 5 pennies for each child; allow time for children to describe and identify the coins. Designate several children as "bankers" to hand out or collect more pennies. Tell stories such as these and have children act them out: "You have 5 pennies, then you earn 3 more. How many pennies do you have now?" "If you spend 4 pennies, how much do you have left?" "You decide to save 3 pennies in the bank. How many pennies do you have left in your purse?" Let children tell about various ways to earn money and spend it as classmates act out the additions and subtractions. Encourage children to extend uses of addition and subtraction with money to the classroom store and housekeeping center.

Add 1, Subtract 1 – and More
Strategies help children determine answers to addition and subtraction. Show five- and six-year old children how to count on 1 and 2 when adding 1 and 2. This is a more efficient procedure than counting two sets, combining them,

then counting all to find the total. Then subtract 1 or 2 by counting back. Expose children to "doubles" for addition (1 + 1, 2 + 2, 3 + 3, 4 + 4, 5 + 5) (Figure 2.6) These facts are easy to learn and are the basis for learning more facts in primary grades (i.e. 6 + 6, 6 + 7).

Addition "Doubles"

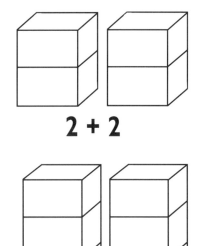

2 + 2

3 + 3

Figure 2.6

Related Children's Books

Use books such as these to promote literacy while introducing and reinforcing ideas of number and operations.

Baker, Keith. 1999. *Quack and Count*. San Diego: Harcourt Brace. (Ducks, rhymes, and addition)

Capucilli, Alyssa Satin. 2001. *Mrs. McTats and Her Houseful of Cats*. New York: M. K.McElderry. (Numbers and number words to 26)

Carlstrom, Nancy White. 1996. *Let's Count It Out, Jesse Bear*. New York: Simon and Schuster. (Counting to 20 at an amusement park)

Cuyler, Margery. 2000. *100th Day Worries*. New York: Simon and Schuster. (Many collections of 100 items)

Hague, Kathleen. 1999. *Numbears: A Counting Book*. Henry Holt. (Bears introduce 1 through 12)

Kitamura, Satoshi. 1986. *When Sheep Cannot Sleep: The Counting Book* (Counting through 22)

Mickelthwait, Lucy. 1992. *I Spy Two Eyes*. New York: Greenwillow. (Numbers of items in art Masterworks)

Murphy, Stuart J. 2000. *Monster Musical Chairs*. New York: Harper Trophy. (6 funny creatures help to subtract 1)

Smith, Maggie. 1995. *Counting Our Way to Maine*. New York: Scholastic. (Counting to 20 on a family trip)

Where It's Going

In the primary grades, children extend work with number to hundreds and thousands. Place value (representing and identifying the ones, tens, hundreds, and thousands that make up numbers) is emphasized, and children learn to read, write, and compare greater numbers. In most school systems, children are expected to master basic facts for addition and subtraction in grades 1 and 2. They also model and learn to work exercises with multidigit addition and subtraction and use these operations in problem solving. Primary children also learn multiplication and division concepts. These operations are emphasized in intermediate grades.

Wrapping It Up

Number and operations are important parts of mathematics for young children. Opportunities to use them abound in the early childhood classroom. Teachers and caregivers can reinforce, extend, and deepen children's understanding and skills with numbers and operations through formal and informal activities. Keeping in mind mathematics processes such as problem solving and communicating, preschool children's work with number and operations can set the firm foundation that is expected in the primary grades.

Chapter 3

Algebra

Four-year-old Kenisha is intent as she arranges shells in piles on the rug. She mumbles to herself: "Big, big, big; this one is big. This one is small and it goes here. This one's all curled up. I can put it here." Ms. Janie notices her work and invites Kenisha to tell two classmates about it. Afterwards, she asks all three children, "How else could you sort the shells?

Algebra for Young Children

Isn't algebra all about solving quadratic equations and graphing curves? Is it only arranging and crossing out x's and y's? Is it too advanced for young children? No, no, and no! For preschool children algebraic thinking concerns sorting, classifying, and ordering objects by observable attributes such as size, shape, number, and other properties. Algebra focuses on working with patterns and describing changes. It also includes using symbols (numerals, words, "boxes") to represent ideas and modeling mathematical ideas with objects, pictures, and symbols (NCTM, 2000, 2001).

Sorting and classifying sets the stage for developing and following rules, a precursor to mathematical

functions. Algebra is about patterns and relationships, and even three-year olds can begin to understand ideas like these. Each school day has a pattern of circle time, indoor time, outdoor time, lunch. A sign is above the door; the door is below the sign.

Activities for Learning about Algebra

Use activities such as the ones here to help children explore algebra.

Sort, Sort, Sort!
Sorting or making groups of like materials are widely used in everyday life. Make available many materials for children to sort. Sets of **post cards, toy silverware, old socks and mittens, seasonal or greeting cards, new and old crayons, wooden beads, shells, rocks, animal pictures, large buttons, small plastic toys, coins, paper shapes, and nuts and bolts of different sizes** are all easy for children to sort by color, shape, size, texture, and other attributes. You might also offer **small boxes, egg cartons, and sorting mats** to help children organize their work. Invite children to share their basis for sorting and think of other ways they might sort the materials. (Figure 3.1)

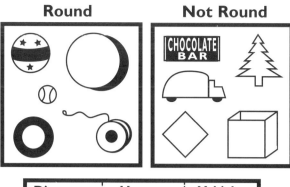

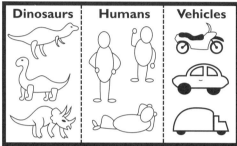

Figure 3.1

Groups of Lids
Widely available, safe, and easy to store, container lids provide an intriguing material for children to sort. Invite families to help you save a variety of **container lids**. Have children sort them by size, color, shape, material, whether they have writing or not, and other attributes. Encourage children to tell each other their sorting rule and follow it in sorting more items. As children gain skill, play "What's the Rule?" Instead of telling sorting rules, children can display sorted items, then ask others to guess how they sorted.

You May Go Now
This activity draws children's attention to a variety of attributes. Dismiss children from the large group by focusing on observable characteristics. Use different attributes on different occasions. Examples: if you're wearing a striped shirt, you may line up now. If your name starts with J or B, you may go to the lunch tables. If you have shoes that tie, it's time for you to wash your hands.

A Look at Pockets
This activity involves counting and comparing as well as sorting. Ask each child to count his or her pockets. Reinforce the use of "zero" for children who have no pockets. Have children check with partners to be sure they have counted correctly. Have them move into groups by numbers of pockets. Lead counting and comparing of the number of children in each group. You might also make a graph or experience story to show your results.

Sorting Cards
Using cards that show many attributes helps children begin to understand that collections may be sorted many ways. Prepare sets of 8-15 cards showing faces with various attributes: curly and straight hair, freckles, hair bows, hats and so on.(Figure 3.2) Introduce the cards by letting children describe what they notice about them. Encourage children to sort the cards many different ways.

23

Figure 3.2

Number Cards: What's on the Other Side?

These sets of cards promote reasoning. Prepare **small cards** with one color on one side and another color on the back. Write or draw numbers, number dots, letters, or shapes on one side. On the other side write or draw things that relate, in a pattern, to those on the front. For example, the front may have numerals 1-9 and the back of each card may show a numeral one greater than the one on the front. (Figure 3.3) You could also use small shapes on the front and larger shapes of the same kind on the back. Show children how to use the cards alone or with partners. They should look at one side of the card, predict what is on the other side, then check by turning the card over. Encourage children to tell the rule that links the fronts and backs of the cards.

Coin Sort

Sorting coins may be done on many different bases. Offer **plastic or real coins** to children who will not put them in their mouths. Invite them to examine and describe the coins. Help children name the coins. Identify their values for children who seem ready. Let children suggest ways to sort the coins, then arrange them in two or more groups. They may sort many ways – by shiny and dull, by size, by type, or by heads and tails.

Clap, Pat, Clap, Pat...

Using body instruments is an easy way to introduce patterns – as well as to get children's attention. Start a pattern of clapping your hands, then patting your thighs. Continue to clap, pat, clap, pat, inviting children to join in. After many repetitions, hold up both of your hands as a signal to stop. Say, "We made a pattern. What did we do?" Accept various answers such as clap, pat, clap, pat; first this, then this; and up, down, up, down. Write ABABABAB on the board as another way of representing the pattern. Next model a clap, clap, pat, clap, clap, pat or AABAAB pattern and have children join in. Repeat the process other times with different simple repeating patterns (ABCABC, ABBABB) and other body instruments.

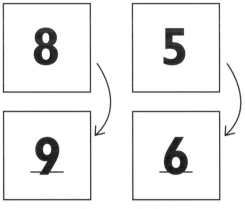

Figure 3.3

Posing in Patterns
At circle time select several children to line up with one sitting, one standing, one sitting, one standing. (Figure 3.4) Have more volunteers join them, maintaining the same pattern of positions. Once all children are included, go down the line having children tell about the positions: sit, stand, sit, stand, and so on. Now make a different pattern with two children facing forward and one back. Encourage children to describe the patterns they have made. What other patterns and poses can the children suggest?

Copy, Describe, Extend, Create
Children's work with patterns often evolves through these stages. First, children must recognize that a pattern exists; next they may copy it with materials or by drawing. Adults can encourage children to talk about and describe the patterns they are making, then extend them. Finally children can create patterns of their own. Use **colored counters or pieces of paper** to begin simple repeating patterns such as green, brown, green, brown (ABAB...) or red, blue, yellow, red, blue, yellow (ABCABC...). Invite children to arrange blocks or pieces of paper below them to make and extend similar patterns. They may arrange the materials in a line, circle, or around the edges of a piece of paper.

Let children tell about their patterns in several ways: by colors, with words such as "first this, then that", or with letters (ABABAB). Finally, encourage children to start and continue different patterns of their own.

Figure 3.4

Block Patterns
Blocks are natural materials for patterning activities. Suggest that children use building blocks, parquetry blocks, or pattern blocks to make repeating patterns. (Figure 3.5) They can line up the blocks on the floor or table top, varying the patterns with blocks in different positions, sizes, and

colors. Encourage children to describe and identify their own patterns and those of others.

Figure 3.5

Patterns with Many Other Materials

Offer different materials such as **wooden beads to string on pipe cleaners, plastic coins, cubes, plastic links, or paper and glue to make paper chains**. Let children use the materials to make various patterns. They might display their patterns on a table or bulletin board, grouping patterns of the same type together. Help them generalize that a repeating pattern such as ABABAB can be shown many different ways.

Number Patterns

Relate models to number symbols with this activity. Provide materials for children to make drawings of themselves, and cats or dogs. Pose the question: How many legs do we have here? Make a **chart** as shown, having children, one at a time, display their drawings of themselves. (Figure 3.6) Discuss patterns seen in the chart: the number of people increases by ones while the number of legs increases by twos. Do the same for cats or dogs; here the number of legs increases by fours. With kindergarten children, you might highlight the number of legs on a hundred chart and have the children describe the patterns they see. Try the same process with children making starfish, insect, spider or octopi models or drawings. With worms, the number of legs will remain zero!

	0	1	2	3	4	5
Worms	0	0	0	0	0	0
People	0	2	4	6	8	10
Dogs	0	4	8	12	16	20
Starfish	0	5	8	15	20	25
Insects	0	6	12	18	24	30
Octopi	0	8	16	24	32	40

LEGS

Figure 3.6

Which Pumpkin?

This activity sharpens children's language skills and logical thinking about attributes. Prepare several **paper pumpkins** such as those shown. (Figure 3.7) Ask children to listen carefully as you offer clues about size, shape, and other attributes for them to identify a pumpkin you are thinking of. As you proceed with the clues, have volunteers remove pumpkins that do not fit the clues. For example: I want a tall pumpkin. I want one with a smiley face. My pumpkin does **not** have a triangular nose. Which one is it?

Figure 3.7

Model a Story, Write a Number Sentence

Kindergarten children develop stronger ideas of addition and subtraction as they work with models and record symbols to match. Provide **counters, pennies**, or **plastic** animals. Invite children to model and solve stories such as these. "Six ducks were swimming in a pond. Two got out of the water. How many are left in the water?" "Aimee had 3 pennies. Mom gave her 2 more. How many pennies does Aimee have now?" Let children share their answers and explain how they figured them out. Show them how to write matching number sentences (6 - 2 = , 3 + 2 =). Have children propose more stories for classmates to model, solve, and write number sentences.

Comparing, Relating

Algebra is about relationships, and children need experiences in comparing and relating. Frequently present situations such as these for children to discuss. Hold up two books of different sizes; help children compare them: this one is taller, that one is shorter; this one is thicker; that one is thinner. Have children look around the room and describe relationships. The flag is above the writing board; the board is under the flag. The door is to the right of the window; the window is to the left of the door.

One Sentence, Many Stories

Help children see that a single number sentence may stand for many different stories. Tell a story such as this one. "Two monkeys were swinging in the tree. Four more came along and began to swing too. How many monkeys were there now?" Help children write a number sentence to match: 2 + 4 = . Have children suggest other stories–silly or realistic–to match the number sentence. They can then draw pictures of their stories and share them with partners of the class.

Changes in the Weather

Discussing the weather daily helps children become aware of subtle and dramatic changes over time. At a regular time each day help children notice the weather and describe it. Ask, "Is the weather about the same as yesterday or has it changed? How?" Prompt children to describe aspects of the weather: temperature (hot, cold, cool, "nice"), sky (clear, overcast, cloudy), and general conditions (rainy, sunny, cloudy, snowy). You might also have children place markers on the calendar to indicate aspects of the weather.

After several days, you might remove markers from the calendar and help children arrange them in a graph-like form. (Figure 3.8) Discuss the results: How many sunny days do the markers show? Were there more sunny or cloudy days? What else could we say about the display of data?

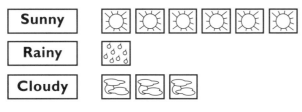

Figure 3.8

How We've Changed!
Let children show their ideas of how they have changed – and will change in the future. Provide **strips of paper**. Guide children to fold the paper in half, then in half again to make four sections. Ask them to draw themselves as babies, as toddlers, and as preschoolers. For the final space, have children draw themselves "when they are big." Let children share their results; encourage them to describe changes in terms of size, abilities, or in other ways.

Related Children's Books

Use books such as these to promote literacy while introducing and reinforcing ideas of algebra.

Baker, Alan. *Gray Rabbit's Odd One Out*. Kingfisher, 1995. (Sorting by different attributes)

Harris, Trudy. *Pattern Fish*. Millbrook Press, 2000. (Many patterns in fish pictures)

Jenkins, Emily. *Five Creatures*. Farrar, Straus & Giroux, 2001. (Sorting family members different ways)

Koomen, Michele. *Patterns: What Comes Next?* Bridgestone, 2001. (Describing and extending patterns)

Murphy, Stuart J. *Beep-Beep, Vroom, Vroom!* Harper Trophy, 2000. (Visual patterns and sequences)

Pluckrose, Henry. *Sorting and Sets*. Gareth Stevens Publishing, 2001. (Sorting by color, kind, shape, and size)

Reid, Margarette S. *The Button Box*. Dutton, 1990. (Sorting buttons many different ways)

Wallwork, Amanda. *No Dodos: A Counting Book of Endangered Animals*. Scholastic, 1993. (Counting as well as patterned borders)

Where It's Going

Work with algebra continues throughout children's schooling and real-world experiences with mathematics. In primary grade mathematics (and science too), children will continue sorting and classifying, sometimes using two attributes such as color and size as they sort. Typically primary children will work with more sophisticated patterns, using number patterns and growing patterns as well as more advanced repeating patterns. They will expand work with number sentences and explore ideas such as the commutative and associative properties as they gain skill in using addition and subtraction. In elementary grades, even more algebra is used as students pursue the related operations of multiplication and division, work with equations and inequalities, generalize about patterns, learn about integers (negative and positive whole numbers), and graph points in the coordinate plane.

Wrapping It Up

Simple ideas of algebra are very appropriate for three- to six-year old children. Sorting and patterning activities are natural for children and relate to everyday life. Work with number sentences and properties enhances quantitative understandings and skills. Presented in engaging activities with concrete materials, such ideas are fun and natural for children – and algebraic explorations expand their thinking skills as well.

Chapter 4

Geometry

Katy and Kevin, four-year old twins, play in the block center. They have built a low fence around some rubber animals. Now Katy embellishes the fence with some half-circle blocks and triangular blocks. Kevin ignores her as Katy says, "These are roundy and these are pointy." Instead Kevin adds more tall blocks, saying, "It needs to be taller with these square ones."

Geometry for Young Children

It's all around us in nature and in objects designed by people. We use it as we decorate our homes, engage in hobbies, and give and receive directions. Yet in school, some adults recall hating and fearing this aspect of mathematics. What is it? Geometry, the spatial side of mathematics.

As they have learned to reach out for objects and people, move about by crawling, walking, and running, children have developed intuitive ideas of space. As they handle objects – books, cups, and balls – children have been exposed to ideas of shape. They have intuitive and informal knowledge of geometry that can be enriched and expanded in the early childhood classroom.

Beyond work with examples of circles, rectangles, and triangles, what content should geometry for young children encompass? Geometry should include attention to **two-and three-dimensional shapes**. Children should build, compare, draw, name, recognize, and begin to describe geometric shapes such as circles, squares, triangles, spheres (balls), pyramids, and rectangular solids (boxes). Younger children tend to visualize shapes as entire entities. Many five- and six-year olds are ready to focus on their attributes. Children also need experiences with **combining shapes and taking them apart**. Children also deal with **spatial relationships**. Words such as near, far, above, below, in front, and behind help children describe **positions** and **relationships among objects**. Gestures and words – and lots of exposure and practice – help children follow and give directions and locate objects.

In addition, young children work with **transformations of shapes**. For example, as a child places puzzle pieces in a frame, she may slide, flip, and turn them to see how they fit together. Using folded paper may serve as an introduction to ideas of **symmetry** - recognizing shapes that have mirrored halves on either side of a line.

Work with geometry heightens awareness of the surroundings and helps children begin to develop an appreciation for the world in which they live – as well as the vocabulary to describe that world. As young children explore geometry, they build a foundation for careers, hobbies, and chores of everyday life. Finally, since geometry can be so engaging, and enjoyable, it helps to develop and sustain positive attitudes toward mathematics in general.

Activities for Learning about Geometry

Use activities such as these to help children explore geometry. Needed materials for activities are shown in bold type.

Throughout the Day
Because the study of geometry builds on and reinforces children's natural curiosity and desire to manipulate objects, it can be used frequently! For example, as children use clay or play dough "food" in the housekeeping center, they might be challenged to make and share "cakes" or "sandwiches" of various shapes." Exploring different ways to break or cut the clay foods can result in much oral language about both shapes and

fractions. As children line up, lead them in forming circles, triangles, and squares with their hands and arms. Post signs written on paper of different shapes.

Positions, Positions, Positions!
As part of their vocabulary growth, children learn many words that indicate position. Work on positional vocabulary often. Discuss objects in the room. Perhaps you can work on a word such as "above" having children note that the calendar is *above* the rug, the helper chart *above* the calendar, the clock *above* the cart, and the ceiling *above* all of these.

Creative movement can also reinforce position words. For example, lead children in stretching *up, up, up*, then *down, down, down*. Have them say *right, right, right* as they move in that direction, then *back, back, back,* and *left, left, left, left*. Have some children form a circle while others dance to music *inside* and *outside* the circle.

Robots
Help children gain skill in following directions in a fun way. Lead a short game in which children move according to directions like robots. Try directions such as these: "Angela, be a robot and move to the front of the room. Carl, you're a robot who moves and stands under the

middle window. Darius, your robot directions are to take the book and put it on the middle bookshelf." As children understand, let them take turns giving directions.

Sort Them

Shapes may be sorted many ways, and reasoning and communication are enhanced by doing so. Provide **paper** or **tagboard shapes** as well as a **variety of cans**, **balls**, and **boxes**. Invite children to sort them several different ways – by flat and not flat; by general types; by shapes with curves and those without; by shapes that slide, shapes that roll and those that do both (Figure 4.1). Let children tell the rules they used for sorting.

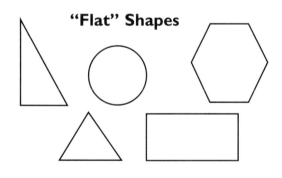

"Flat" Shapes

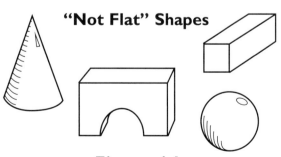

"Not Flat" Shapes

Figure 4.1

"Meet the Shapes" Puppets

It's fun when a puppet takes a turn in teaching. Prepare **simple paper bag puppets** to introduce a few shapes. Let the puppets "introduce" themselves to the children and ask the children if they know what their names might be. Let children take turns using the puppets to point out classroom objects that have similar shapes to those of the puppets.

Next have children make their own paper bag shape puppets. Encourage them to name their puppets and tell about them. Let children use the puppets to "help" in sorting shapes.

Potato Prints

Geometric designs and patterns are easy to make using potatoes and paint. Cut several potatoes and carve out geometric shapes. Show children how to hold the potato by the uncut part, dip it lightly in paint, and then print onto paper. Children can make designs or repeating patterns.

Shape Walk 1: Shape Hunt

A shape hunt can make children more aware of shapes – and sizes – in the environment. Lead children on a walk around the school or neighborhood. Encourage them to point out shapes and sizes they notice and to describe their locations – a billboard may be a huge rectangle above our heads; a pipe may look like a long, thin cylinder. Take notes of shapes the children see. Back in the classroom, help children review the findings as you write an experience story about the walk. To vary the shape hunt, hide small paper shapes around the classroom. Let children search for them, bring them to the group area, then sort them by color and shape.

Shape Walk 2: Walk Across
Use a permanent marker to draw shapes on sturdy plastic shelf paper or an 18-inch wide strip of plastic tablecloth. Lay the strip on the floor. Invite children to walk across it, naming the shapes as they come to them. Or let a child walk across the shapes while the others name the shapes. Offer directions such as "Walk across on the circles only." or "Walk on the triangles while we count them." Leave the display in an out-of-the-way place for children to use independently. You might also make a tabletop display for children to use to make dolls "walk across" or drive toy cars on.

Shape Walk 3:
Walk and Name Them
A banner with shapes takes up little room, but offers more exposure to shapes. (Figure 4.2) Post a paper or plastic strip with pictures of shapes on the wall, perhaps near the place where children line up. Demonstrate how to walk along the banner of shapes, point to the shapes, and name

them. Encourage children to walk along the banner with partners and discuss the shapes they see.

Figure 4.2

Shape Walk 4
Yet another version of the shape walk gets children physically involved. Use **masking tape** to outline several large shapes, perhaps a large triangle, square, hexagon, and rectangle, on the floor. Let children walk around them, perhaps clapping as they turn each corner. Let children "walk the shapes" in free time or give directions such as "Go to the triangle and walk around it in baby steps." or "Walk around the rectangle and count its sides as you go."

Imprints
This sensory activity lets children predict and verify results. Use oil-based clay or play dough and small objects in distinct shapes. Show children how to flatten the clay, then press an object into it and remove the object to see an imprint of its shape. After some experience, encourage them to predict what an imprint will look like before making it.

"Show Me" Shapes

With verbal and visual clues, this activity lets each child participate. Give each child in a large or small group several **small paper shapes**; each child need not have the same ones. Hold up a shape and say, "If you have one like this, hold it up and show me." Visually check the children. Continue the process, asking children to show you various shapes. From time to time, pause and ask children to name or describe their shapes. Vary your requests by describing shapes to be shown. Try letting the children take turns asking their groupmates to show various shapes.

Make a Shape – with Magnets

Simple materials – **strips of magnet and an old steel cookie sheet** – provide for much sensory learning. (Figure 4.3) Demonstrate how to attract a **shape picture** to the magnet board with a piece of magnet, then choose other magnet strips to cover the picture and form the shape. Say, "Now I'll make another shape of the same kind." and use more magnet strips to make a second figure of different sizes or proportions. Help children name the shapes you have made. Make the materials available for children's independent work. Partners might take turns, with one making a shapes and the other naming and describing, then changing roles.

Figure 4.3

Yarn Shapes

Using yarn is another easy and satisfying way for children to make shapes. Using a **felt or flannel board and short pieces of thick yarn**, show children how to arrange the yarn to form shapes. Turn them loose to make more shapes, encouraging them to name or describe the shapes as they work. Children can also use longer pieces of yarn (6-10 feet) and work together holding the yarn to form shapes.

Pipe Cleaner Shapes

Inexpensive **pipe cleaners** are reusable materials for building flat and three-dimensional shapes. Show children how to make simple shapes by bending and combining one or more pipe cleaners. Allow time for them to create several shapes. Discuss the shapes and help children name them. Let children sort the shapes they have made.

Shape Twins 1: See and Match
This visual discrimination task challenges children to notice attributes of shapes. Collect a variety of pairs of like shapes – **plastic 2-D pieces in geometric shapes; paper shapes; wood, plastic or foam 3-D shapes**. Set up a center with pairs of shapes and show children how to find "twins" or pairs of shapes that are alike. Encourage children to self-and-peer check, placing shapes side by side or atop each other to be sure they are alike. As children work, occasionally ask them to explain how they know their shapes are alike.

Shape Twins 2: Make a Hidden Match
Here is another way to build visual discrimination skills. Hide four or five plastic, foam, or paper shapes under a towel or cloth, and display matching shapes in plain view. Point out one of the visible shapes, and let children take turns feeling the shapes under the cloth, trying to find its "twin." When the child thinks she has found the matching shapes, let her display it while other children tell whether they agree. Help the children name and describe the shapes as they are matched. Offer the activity for independent work.

Slide, Flip, and Turn
Here's a way to help children understand transformations or movements of shapes. Give each child a **paper shape**, colored on one side. Illustrate how to slide the shapes through the air as you ask the children to slide their shapes "straight across," "up and down," or in a diagonal along the floor. Choose a child or two to lead showing a way to slide the shape and have the others try to follow.

Next show how to lay the shape on the floor, then flip it over. Children will see the "backsides" of their shapes. With another flip, the shape will be on its "right side" again. Let several children flip their shapes while the others follow.

Finally demonstrate how to lay the shape on the floor and turn the shape around one of its corners. Encourage children to describe what their shapes look like after various turns. Triangles for example, may be described as "right side up" and "up side down" as children turn them 180° at a time.

Play music and let children freely dance with their shapes, then move to the music as you ask them to slide, turn, and flip their shapes.

Nibble It, Change It
Children love to make shapes of **soda crackers or graham crackers**! Provide crackers and let children (with clean hands) feel along their straight edges and square corners. Let children nibble their crackers to make rectangles, then smaller squares. Offer each child a second

cracker to nibble, then show a new shape to the group.

Fold it, Tear It, Punch It, and ...

Introduce the idea of symmetry with folded paper. Give each child a **small square or rectangle of paper**. Show them how to fold it in half, then unfold to look at the parts and describe them. Have children fold their papers again and tear through both layers, leaving the fold line intact. When children unfold, let them show their results. They will see the same shape as mirrored halves. They have made a symmetrical design. Let children repeat the process tearing or cutting their papers in different ways. You might show five- and six-year old children how to cut heart or butterfly shapes from folded paper.

You can also let children dribble paint on one half of a folded paper, close the paper and press lightly, and then open it to see the symmetrical result. Another variation is to have children fold their papers, punch some holes through both layers, predict the total number, and unfold the paper to count and verify.

Shapes from Home

Examples of geometry abound in everyday life. Helping children find examples of them in their homes makes them more aware that geometry is all around us. Ask that children find several examples of shapes you are studying at home. For example, after introducing circles, ask children to find examples of circles where they live and have an older person help them sketch two or three examples. Request that, if possible, children bring a circular item from home to show at school. Let children show their drawings and tell about their examples, then arrange a sharing table for children to display their circular items. Help children remember to take their items home after a day or two.

Geometry Collage

Working with precut shapes, children can make creative designs. Cut a variety of paper shapes. Let children glue them to paper to make abstract designs or pictures of real objects. Allow time for children to present their creations to the class. For a home project, send home a glue stick, several paper shapes, and a request that family members help the child name and discuss the shapes, arrange them, and glue them to paper. They might want to make a design or add features with crayon or pencil to make a picture of a person, animal, or scene. Back at school, invite children to show their completed collages and tell about how the family member helped them. Display the shape collages for a few days, then send them home again.

Related Children's Books

Use books such as these to promote literacy while introducing and reinforcing ideas of geometry.

Cohen, Caron Lee. 1996. *Where is the Fly?* New York: Greenwillow. (Positions and spatial relationships)

Crimi, Carolyn. 1995. *Outside, Inside.* New York: Simon and Schuster. (Many position words)

Dunbar, Fiona. 1991. *You'll Never Guess!* New York: Dial. (Guessing shapes from their shadows.)

Ernesto, Lilly, & Hendry, Linda. 1993. *Look Inside.* Lexington MA: D. C. Heath (Positions in many settings)

Grifalconi, Ann. 1986. *The Village of Round and Square Houses.* Boston: Little Brown. (African houses in different shapes.)

Hoban, Tana. 1996. *Shapes, Shapes, Shapes.* New York: Greenwillow. (Photos of objects of different shapes)

McDonald, Suse. 1994. *Sea Shapes.* San Diego: Harcourt Brace. (Many shapes in sea creatures)

Where It's Going

In the primary grades, children focus on a greater variety of plane and solid shapes and their attributes. They learn to figure area and perimeter and extend their work with fractions. In intermediate grades and middle school, students explore points, lines, planes, angles, and spatial relationships. They make and investigate conjectures about properties and relationships of shapes. Work with geometry is further extended in high school with topics such as graphing equations, using formulas, and learning to write formal proofs.

Wrapping It Up

Because it is all around us, geometry is a natural part of each child's world. It is one of the ideas – along with number – that is at the "core of mathematics" for the early childhood years (NCTM, 2000, p. 77). Work with geometry complements numerical and quantitative concepts and presents a realistic, full view of mathematics. Work with geometry also contributes to development of children's spatial intelligence and their abilities to describe where they are and what they are doing. It helps children develop "an intuitive feel for one's surroundings and objects in them" (NCTM, 1989, p. 49).

Chapter 5

Measurement

Inspired by a creative movement exercise, three-year old Kelly stretches, raises his arms, and skips around the playground announcing, "I'm tall! I'm taller! I'm even taller!" His caregiver smiles, realizing that Kelly shows beginning understanding of an important measurement concept.

Measurement for Young Children

"Measurement is one of the most widely used applications of mathematics. It bridges two main areas of school mathematics– geometry and number" (NCTM, 2000). For young children measurement activities relate to everyday skills and processes and at the same time develop ideas that will be formalized and expanded in later schooling.

As they work with measurement, children compare and order objects on the basis of attributes such as length, capacity or weight. At first, comparisons are direct – placing one object beside another to judge heights or holding objects in both hands to feel which seems heavier. Ordering involves putting three or more things in order, perhaps from a basket that holds the least to one that holds the most. Language development is important. Words such as "large, deep, heavy, and longer" and questions such as "How long? How hot? and How much surface is covered?" help children recognize and describe measurement attributes.

The process of measurement involves linking a number and a unit (5 pounds, 14 centimeters, 2 hours). Typically a single unit is reiterated or repeated to measure something larger than the unit, for example, measuring height in inches. All measurement is approximate, and adults can model this idea using words such as "those are <u>about</u> the same length" or "that's <u>between</u> 5 and 6 paper clips long. " In kindergarten non-standard measurement is important. For example, young children use units such as hands, their own feet, paper clips, and blocks to determine lengths. Three- to six year-olds should also informally use standard units such as inches, cups, and pounds as well as standard tools (rulers, thermometers, scales, and measuring cups) in daily activities.

What measurement attributes should young children explore? NCTM (2000) recommends that they recognize and work with attributes of length, volume, weight, area, and time. As they compare, order, and measure with non-standard units, children also apply and refine number sense in estimating measurements.

Activities for Learning about Measurement

Use activities such as these to help children explore measurement. Needed materials for activities are shown in bold type.

Calendar Time!
Spending a few minutes on calendar time each day lets children visit and revisit many math concepts. Use a large calendar with movable markers of different colors or shapes. Markers will show dates: they also can be used to create repeating patterns with color and show seasonal motifs or geometric shapes. Invite children to describe the patterns as they emerge. Assign calendar helpers to place the markers and announce the date. Let children predict what tomorrow's marker will look like. Help the class re-read the number and tell its ordinal name (18 means the 18th day of the month).

You may want children to repeat the full date with its day of the week, month, and year. You might use a feltboard "weather doll" with clothes for different temperatures and kinds of weather. Occasionally mention the season and compare temperatures. "Is it as hot as yesterday? Is it warmer or cooler outside than inside?" Calendar time may be an opportunity to work with the number of days of school, preview the day's activities, or introduce any new vocabulary words for the day.

A Week Line
Names of days and the terms "yesterday, today, tomorrow" can be confusing, but a week line can help to clarify them. (Figure 5.1) At calendar time as you invite children to repeat the date, have a volunteer stand on its name on a **week line** made of plastic shelf paper or strip of plastic table cloth or shower curtain. Have the child take a step to the left as the class tells yesterday's name and 2 steps to the right to find tomorrow's date. Place the week line in a location were children can walk along it and say the names of the days of the week. You may also attach the week line to a wall and paper clip notes to it.

Figure 5.1

Times of Day
Daily routines are important for young children: discussing them helps to develop concepts of time. Post your daily schedule and periodically review it with children. Discuss the order of events and tell which occur before and after notable events such as outdoor time or lunch. Use ordinal numbers to identify what you do first, second, third, and last each day.

Longer Time, Shorter Time
Which takes longer: making a pizza or eating it? Putting on jacket or shoes? Children can predict, then act out or time events to find out. Discuss how long a task such as making a snack might take, refer to the clock, and record a starting time. (Figure 5.2) Involve children in the task and then note the ending time. For tasks that take just a short time, lead children in slowly counting to gauge the time. Over a week you might list and review times for several events. Let children identify the longer and shorter times for them.

Longer Times	Shorter Times
eat lunch	get a drink
read 5 stories	read 1 story
play outdoors	line up to go out
nap time	clean up time

Figure 5.2

How Long Does It Take?
How long can you stand on one foot? How many times can you write your name in a minute? Explore questions like these. Let children make some predictions, then slowly count or watch a clock with a second hand to time classmates. (Figure 5.3)

We counted to see how long we could stand on one foot

Jack - 8

Vicki - 10

Meg - 7

Charita - 5

Pedro - 9

Vicki stood the longest time.

Figure 5.3

Monthly Posters
Monthly posters are a way of keeping track of time, events, and changes. (Figure 5.4) Use half sheets of poster board to make **monthly mini-posters** displaying the name of the month, lists of special events, birthdays for the month, notes about the weather, and taped-on natural specimens. Display the posters in a line on the wall. Review them every few weeks, emphasizing names of months and seasonal changes, and recognizing children's birthdays.

Figure 5.4

Taller, Shorter, Bigger, Smaller
Help children use and represent measurement words with creative movements. Play lively music and have children march in place. Encourage them to stand tall, then raise their arms to model being even taller. Next lead children in stooping and bending their legs to "get shorter." Let children show how to spread their arms to make their bodies wider and wider, then pull in their arms to "get narrow" again. Have children show how they can "grow bigger", then "get smaller" again. Let children pose and tell some words that apply to their stances.

Big Figures
Life-sized figures are fun to make and display; in the process, children use measurement ideas. Have children lie down on large paper and trace around them. Have each child look at the outline as you acknowledge how tall she is. Let the child trace or point to her height and other locations such as the width of the shoulders or length of a foot. Over the next few days, let children color clothes and features on the figures. Post them in a line outside the classroom or along a wall. Discuss the figures, comparing heights, length of hair, and recognizing special features of each one. Large figures make a great display for an art fair or family open house.

About The Same Length
This measurement activity is fun to do outdoors. Invite children to trace over their palms, from wrist to the end of the fingers with a finger. State that this distance could be called the length of a hand. Ask each child to find an object or two that is about this same length. After children find their objects, let them show them to the group, holding the objects up to match, or nearly match, the length of a hand. Conduct a similar activity in the classroom with children finding objects about as long a foot or finger.

41

Measuring Lengths

After they measure lengths with a variety of units, children can compare results. Specify a distance such as the length of a room. Let several children step off the length as the class counts their numbers of steps. Record the results and encourage children to discuss why the number of steps may have varied. Lead children to decide they might increase or decrease the number of steps for the length (Take smaller steps to get a greater number, longer steps to produce a smaller number.)

Repeat the process, letting children measure other distances in steps. They might also measure the length of a table or rug in "hands" or book lengths. Also let them measure lengths and widths of small objects with cubes or paper clips.

Estimate and Measure

After children have had some experience with nonstandard measurement of length, help them estimate lengths too. Use several pieces of yarn and stretch them out on the rug. Hold a measuring unit such as a paper clip or connecting cube near one of the pieces of yarn. Record children's estimates of about how many cubes or paper clips long the yarn is. Let children use the unit to measure the piece of yarn. Record the results and use them to make estimates for subsequent pieces of yarn.

Dino Dimensions

Many dinosaurs were of impressive size. Help children picture their sizes with this activity. Use a factual book about dinosaurs and share information about their sizes. For example, work outdoors using the fact that Shantungosaurus was 52 feet long. Cut pieces of yarn 10 feet long, then let children stretch them out to represent the dinosaur's length. Have children hold hands and see how many it takes to be about this same length. Let children choose other dinosaur facts and help to decide how to represent some of the sizes.

Heights and Weights

Record heights and weights for school records and family information – and to demonstrate uses of measuring tools. Working individually with children, use a tape measure affixed to the wall to measure heights and a step-on scale to measure weights. You might let children get on the scale, observe the reading on the dial, then hold a backpack and see the reading increase. Five- and six-year olds can make small "ID cards" with names and self-portraits; they can copy their heights and weights onto the cards.

How Heavy?

Weight is the measurement attribute that answers the question "how heavy." Use backpacks or paper sacks full of objects such as books, styrofoam bits (inside a plastic bag), and extra clothing. Let children lift them and compare weights. Fill small-sized paper bags with different objects: marbles, sand, crumpled paper, water in a closed container, and Easter grass. Let children lift the bags and tell which are heavier and lighter, then arrange the bags in order from lightest to heaviest. Children might guess what is inside of each bag. Let children lift them, compare weights, and use words such as "heavy" and "lighter" to describe them. On the playground, let children fill buckets with sand, lift them, and transport them in wagons for easier carrying.

Balancing Act

A simple **balance scale** provides for hours of experimentation. Show children how to place different **small objects** in the pans of the balance. The heavier objects will make the pan go down. If the pans balance, the objects are about the same weight. Help children record results as they predict which objects are heavier, then use nonstandard units such cubes or pennies to balance various objects.

Pouring and Describing

Working at a sand or water table is fun and relaxing for children, but it also exposes them to ideas of capacity and volume − both spatial concepts. Provide a variety of **plastic containers** as well as **strainers, short pieces of plastic hoses, and other props**. For a smaller-scale setup, you might use small dried beans or birdseed as a "pourable solid" in a plastic tub. Set some ground rules such as sharing materials and keeping sand or water in the table. Encourage children to explore and tell each other what they are doing. Ask questions such as "Which one do you think holds more?" and "Which container holds the least?" to prompt children's thinking.

Will It Fit?

Children can notice, then predict and verify volumes of various containers. Help children notice and describe the sizes of various storage containers in the classroom. Which seems to hold the most? Which containers hold smaller and larger items? Offer a variety of **boxes, bowls, and tubs**. Let children use classroom objects such as handfuls of crayons, sackfuls of blocks, and stacks of blocks. Discuss whether sets of specific objects will fit in certain containers. Let children tell what they think, then try it out.

Three Bears, Three Billy Goats, or...

Read a story that features characters in different sizes. Have children act out the characters, making their bodies smaller and larger. Show props such as bowls or paper hats and beds: let children decide which character might use each item. Encourage children to compare the pictures and props, using words such as big, small, medium, middle-sized, longer, shorter, holds more, and holds less.

Warmer, Cooler

Children use words like these as they start thinking about temperature. Lead a discussion of favorite foods. Make a list of suggested foods that are served hot and cold. Have children describe what they wear and typical activities for warmer and cooler weather. Let children make pictures of hot and cold or warmer and cooler things.

Introducing the Concept of Area

Area is a measure of surface, a concept frequently encountered throughout the day. Have children role-play situations in which they wash a tabletop, fill an entire paper with paint, or sweep the floor. Use "area" to describe an entire flat surface. Tell area riddles such as these and let children find the locations. "It is above us, painted white and very flat (ceiling)." "On this area we hang artwork and notices (bulletin board)." "Tiles and the rug cover this area (floor)." Provide **paper** for children to make "grassy areas" or "water areas" for plastic animals. Arrange **large paper shapes** on the floor and let children walk across

them following directions such as these: "Step only on the circular areas." "This time walk across the areas with straight sides."

Many Measurement Words

Be sure to use measurement vocabulary as it applies throughout the day. Words such as "more, less, bigger, smaller, empty, half full, and full" may apply at snack time. On an outdoor walk discuss objects that are bigger, wider, or shorter than others. Use "warmer" and "cooler" to compare temperatures in the sun and in the shade. Discuss activities that take longer and shorter times: anticipate events with phrases such as "tomorrow," and "next week." In science experiences, help children count and measure to quantify findings. As children prepare their belongings to go home, talk about the weight of their packs and other items.

A Tool Kit

Experiences are essential as children learn about measurement, and a toolkit adds much to dramatic play. Prepare a kit with "real" props such as a **ruler, measuring tapes, sturdy thermometer, old clock, plastic measuring cups and spoons, and fishing scale**. Demonstrate how to use some of the tools and describe workers and hobbyists who may use them. Make the kit available in the block or housekeeping center.

Related Children's Books

Use books such as these to promote literacy while introducing and reinforcing ideas of measurement.

Carle, Eric. 1994. *The Hungry Caterpillar*. New York: Putnam. (Days of the week)

Carter, David A. 1988. *How Many Bugs in a Box?* New York: Simon & Schuster. (Counting and capacity)

Dunbar, Joyce. 2000. *The Very Small*. San Diego: Harcourt. (Comparing bears' sizes)

George, Jean Craighead. 1998. *Morning, Noon, and Night*. New York: Harper Collins. (Times of day)

Lively, Penelope. 1999. *One, Two, Three, Jump!* New York: McElderry. (Lengths and sizes)

Miller, Margaret. 1996. *Now I'm Big*. New York: Greenwillow. (Comparing children's sizes and abilities)

Most, Bernard. 1994. *How Big Were the Dinosaurs?* New York: Silver Burdett and Ginn. (Dinosaur sizes related to children)

Tafari, Nancy. 1999. *A Twelve Months Rhyme*. New York: Scholastic. (Months of the year)

Where It's Going

In the primary grades, children continue their work with comparing, ordering, and using non-standard measurements. They also learn to use rulers to measure in standard units – inches and centimeters. Children compare quantities to standard measures such as cups, pounds, and liters and begin to read thermometers. In intermediate grades, children expand the scope of standard measures using tools with more precision. They develop and use formulas for computing measures such as area, perimeter, and volume. In middle school students use ratios to convert measurements and use measurement in advanced problem solving.

Wrapping It Up

Measurement is a practical content area and one in which most children are interested. Measurement ideas are especially useful in children's work with early childhood science. Because it provides opportunities for vocabulary development, connecting to the real world, and problem solving, measurement is a topic that can be incorporated into many thematic units throughout the year.

Chapter 6

Data Analysis and Probability

Ms. Washington is pleased at how well her day care children responded when they discussed names for their new gerbil and then voted for a favorite name. However, she found that when she listed suggested names and asked children to raise their hands for a favorite, many children raised their hands every time. She solved the problem by reading the suggested gerbil names, then giving each child a block to cast as a vote when she called out the names. She plans to use this "one person, one vote" procedure again.

Data Analysis and Probability for Young Children

In our information-oriented world, it is not surprising that collection, organization, and interpretation of data has entered the early childhood curriculum. As a real and engaging topic for three- to six-years olds, data analysis involves posing questions and gathering data to answer questions about the children, their opinions, and their surroundings. Children apply their knowledge of comparing, counting, and sorting and classifying as they work with

data or information. Children can represent data with objects, pictures, and symbols. They can describe parts of sets of data. Even young children can begin to explore ideas related to probability or chance, discussing events they have experienced. For example, they can tell whether they think it might rain tomorrow, whether they will have pizza for lunch, or whether a spinner is "fair" or not. (NCTM, 2000).

As children become involved in asking questions and making displays of results, moving from representing data with real, concrete objects to pictures and symbols helps them understand the process. The children might show their snack time beverage choices by standing in groups or rows with their milk or juice cartons. (Figure 6.1) They could then arrange the cartons for a smaller, easier-to-read display. A more abstract representation of the same data would be for children to draw pictures of their beverage containers or place their nametags in a display of their choice. Over time data should be displayed in groups, horizontal rows, and vertical columns.

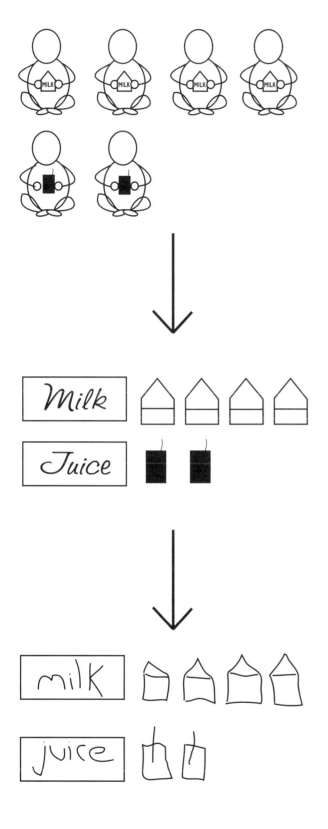

For young children it is a good idea to use a limited number of categories for displaying data. Two or three choices are fine to start with: plain milk, chocolate milk, or juice – or red objects and objects that are not red. In some situations "Other" makes a useful category name. Once a data display is made, open-ended questions like "What does our graph tell us?" or "What did we find out?" invite discussion of results. After some open-ended discussion, if children do not initiate it, the teacher or caregiver can then lead children in counting and comparing numbers of items from various categories.

As children work with data analysis and probability, opportunities abound to use math processes of problem solving, reasoning, representing ideas, communicating, and relating to the real world. Here is an example in addition to the one about naming the class gerbil.

Kenisha is proud of her new baby brother and she knows that her friend LaToya also has a younger brother. The girls ask how many other children also have little brothers. At circle time Ms. Washington asks each child whether he or she has a little brother. She records the children's names in categories. She makes tallies for the same data and helps

Figure 6.1

the children recount the tally marks and write numbers for each.

Ms. Washington asks, "What did we learn from this?" and they discuss the results, reviewing that 6 reported having younger brothers and 8 did not – fewer had little brothers than did. Ms. Washington queries, "How many told about their little brothers?" She leads the group in counting all the tallies and all the children to be sure the numbers are the same. After this, Pedro suggests finding out who, like him, has a younger sister, so Ms. Washington decides to make this a part of tomorrow's circle time discussion.

Activities for Learning About Data Analysis and Probability

Use activities such as these to help children explore data and probability. Materials needed for activities are shown in bold type.

Our Favorites
Letting children show their favorites provides an almost endless supply of topics for graphs. (Figure 6.2) Questions such as "What was your favorite thing on our trip to the store?" "What's your favorite color?" "What's a favorite thing to do on the weekend?" capture children's interest and let

them express their opinions. Pose such a question and let children tell their favorites. Have children stand in groups, then sit in rows according to their choices. Ask "What did we find out about our favorite ___?" and invite several responses. You might also let children draw pictures of their favorite __ and arrange these to form a graph.

Figure 6.2

48

Photo-graphs

Personalized and easy to make, photo-graph markers can be used over and over. Use recent **photos** of children. (Figure 6.3) (You might use class photos or take pictures of children in groups of two or three and cut the photos apart to show each child's face.) Let children glue their pictures to squares of paper or tape them to small milk or juice cartons. Use the pictures as graph markers for any sort of graph. Letting children draw their own graph markers is another approach.

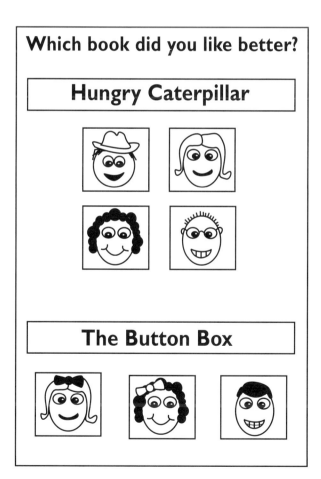

Figure 6.3

Socks and Shoes

Children can find many ways to compare and sort themselves by the types of shoes and socks they are wearing. Let children show off their shoes, soles and all. Help them describe features of their shoes: colors, fasteners, sole patterns, and so on. Choose an attribute and have children sort themselves into groups based on presence or absence of the characteristic. Discuss the real graph the children have made, perhaps starting with the question, "What does the graph tell us?" Choose another way to sort the children, perhaps, "Are you wearing socks or not?" and repeat the process.

Our Shirts

Other easily obtained and interesting data comes from children's shirts or tops. Help children discuss their tops – "Do they have short sleeves, long sleeves or no sleeves?" "What patterns can we see in the tops and which are plain?" "Which children are wearing sweaters and which are not?" Ask for suggestions on how the data could be shown and help children make a graph, chart or other display. Lead counting of the number in each category. Compare numbers: "Which category has the greatest number? The least? Are any numbers the same?"

Graphing Trash
After you clean up trash from the classroom or a neighborhood walk, look carefully at some of it, then make a graph. You might sort trash by size – large, medium, and small items, material – plastic, paper, metal and "other;" or by whether it can be recycled or not. Have children lay their trash items in groups to make a real graph of it. After discussing the graph, be sure that children wash their hands.

Handfuls or Spoonfuls
Here's an opportunity for five-and six-year olds to work with numerical data. Supply materials such as **small blocks or cubes, large beans, or styrofoam peanuts**. Let children take handfuls of the material and count the numbers they got. To help them in counting, perhaps you want to direct children to make any groups of ten they can. Using square **self-adhesive notes**, help each child write his or her number. Ask, "How can we organize the numbers?" Follow up on suggestions, perhaps having the children place their numbers in order from least to greatest or placing them in categories such as 10, less than 10, or more than 10. Invite predictions of how many of the small objects children think they could hold in another handful. Let children take their second handfuls, record numbers, and compare the results of the first and second trials.

Another time, let children use spoons to scoop up the materials and compare numbers per spoonful.

Birthday Display
On-going recognition of children's birthdays is also a chance to display data. Use your monthly miniposters (Chapter 5) or use the children's records to find out birthday months. Make a **chart or graph** of the data. (Figure 6.4) To help children interpret the data, ask questions such as these. "Whose birthdays are in June?" "How many birthdays are there in April and May?" "How many

Do a cake display for birthdays OR a chart

January   February   March   April

— OR —

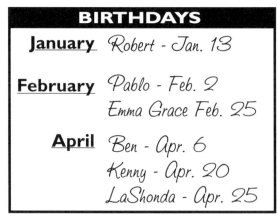

Figure 6.4

50

more birthdays are in September than October?" "Which month has no birthdays?"

Letters in Our Names
Counting, comparing, and graphing letters in names adds to literacy as well as math skills. Display children's **name cards** and help children read them. (Figure 6.5) Let children point out letters they know. Lead counting of the number of letters in first names. Have each child count his or her letters and place the card in a category such as names with fewer than 5 letters, names with 5 letters, or names with more than 5 letters. Discuss the graph. At other times make graphs with the name cards according to whether they have an e or not, by the numbers of letters in last names, or by the total number of letters.

How many letters are in your name?

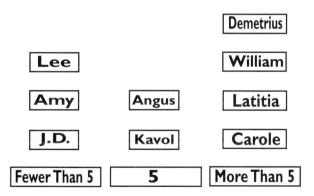

Figure 6.5

Poll Takers
With a clipboard and graph form, pairs of children can poll classmates – and feel very grownup in the process. Work with two children to develop a question for a graph. Help them write words or symbols for the graph categories. Then let the children poll several classmates during a time when children are working at centers. At a large group time, let the "pollsters" explain their results.

Float and Sink
After children explore science phenomenon, they can make a chart or graph to record results. Work with small groups. Offer a **variety of small objects**–rubber bands, paper clips, bits of styrofoam and sponge, crayons, pencils, rocks, twigs, bits of paper, and so on. Let children predict which objects will float or sink. Record the predictions. Have children take turns placing the objects in a **bowl of water** to see if they float or sink, then placing them in rows according to the results. Discuss the results, letting children compare predictions and results, name objects that floated or sank, and count and compare the numbers in the categories.

Does It Attract or Not?
To record results from another science investigation, use magnets and classroom objects. Show children how a magnet will attract objects made of iron and steel, but will not attract or "stick to" a crayon

or piece of yarn. Invite predictions of other objects that will and won't stick to the magnet, then let children test the objects with the magnet. Make charts or graphs of predictions and results. Ask, "What did we learn?" and let children tell what they found about magnetic attraction as well as making a comparison of the numbers of objects.

A Natural Collection
After children have observed and collected **natural specimens**, let them display the specimens in a real graph. Take a nature walk and, in an area where children can collect a few specimens, let each child pick up a pinecone, twig, leaf, or similar item. Back in the classroom, let children tell about their specimens and suggest ways to categorize them – perhaps by type, color, or size. Have children arrange the items in a real graph on the science table or tape or pin the item, in categories, to a bulletin board. With the children, write a story about the experience.

Graphing Plant Growth
Combine science, measurement, and graphing with this simple activity in which strips of paper are used to depict plant growth. It may also serve as an introduction to a vertical bar graph. As children complete a project of growing plants, let them use **paper strips** to measure their seedling's growth. Show children

how to hold a strip of paper next to the seedlings and tear off the strip to represent its approximate height. Have children tape or glue the strips to another paper to make a graph. (Figure 6.6) If you start the process the day you plant the seeds, for a few days, no stems and leaves will be visible, so there will be no bars on the graph. Help children look at the graph to see how high their plants have grown. Are there times when the seedlings have grown faster than at other times?

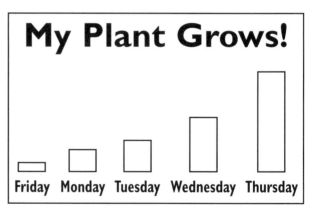

Figure 6.6

What Will Happen?
Help children understand that some things happen all the time, some things some of the time, and some

things never happen. Use two prepared **spinners** or make them of cardboard with a brad and large paper clip for the moving spinner. Color one spinner background all red and the other half red and half blue. Discuss questions like these and note children's predictions. "Will we get red every time we spin the red spinner?" "Will we ever get yellow?" "What do you think will happen with the spinner that is red and blue?" Let children take turns spinning as you record results. Use probability words such as *always*, *sometimes*, and *never* as you talk about results.

More Work with Probability
Follow up on experiences with probability and spinners with focus on special vocabulary that helps people describe probability or chance. Talk about words such as *sometimes*, *maybe*, *always*, and *never* and what they tell us about the likelihood of things happening. Engage children making a list of things that always happen, usually happen, sometimes happen, and never happen. Review the list, returning to it once or twice more to solicit more ideas from the children.

What's in the Bag?
Logical thinking about events can occur with this activity. Prepare a "**mystery**" **bag** with nine red **blocks** and one white block inside. Tell children that there are ten cubes in the bag. They will takes turns pulling a block out of the bag noting its color, then returning the cube to the bag. Shake the bag after each block is shown, and no peeking at the entire contents of the bag! After several children have had a turn sampling the contents of the bag, let several tell what they think about the colors of the bag's blocks and why they think so. You might record some of their responses before you reveal the contents of the bag. Repeat the activity another day, perhaps using equal numbers of colors and a combination of seven red and three white blocks.

Related Children's Books

Use books such as these to promote literacy while introducing and reinforcing ideas of data and probability.

Franco, Betsy. 1997. *Sorting All Sorts of Socks*. Mountain View, CA: Creative Publications. (Purposes of sorting)

Giganti, Paul, Jr. 1988. *How Many Snails?* New York: Greenwillow. (Focus on attributes for sorting)

Hoban, Tana. 1984. *Is It Rough? Is It Smooth? Is It Shiny?* New York: Greenwillow. (Attributes and categories to invite graphing)

Miller, Margaret. 1992. *Where Does It Go?* New York: Greenwillow. (Deciding which set familiar objects belong to)

Mollel, Tololwam. 1999. *My Rows and Piles of Coins*. New York: Clarion (An African boy sorts and saves money for a bike)

Nagda, Ann Whitehead & Bickle, Cindy. 2000. *Learning to Graph from a Baby Tiger*. New York: Henry Holt. (A story of a real tiger with graphs included)

Sisulu, Elinor Batzat. 1996. *The Day that Gogo Went to Vote*. Boston: Little Brown. (A South African grandmother casts her first vote.)

Where It's Going

In the primary grades, children continue making and interpreting graphs. They branch out to bar graphs and simple circle graphs. They learn some simple statistical terms such as range and median, and they explore concepts of chance such as "equally likely." In intermediate grades and middle grades students use an even wider range of more complex graphs such as stem and leaf plots, histograms, and box and whiskers graphs. They learn about measures of central tendency such as mean, mode, and median. Older students learn about experimental and mathematical probability for a variety of events. In many high schools courses on statistics are available. Data analysis and probability are also parts of other advanced math courses.

Wrapping It Up

Making and interpreting displays of data and understanding the chances of events are practical parts of living in our information society. Part of a broad mathematics curriculum for young children, data analysis and probability are interesting, appropriate topics. Working with data lets children use their growing language and reasoning skills as well as skills in sorting, counting, and comparing numbers. Probability or chance is a part of real life, and introducing it to young children starts a foundation of mathematical ideas to be used for years to come.

References

Andrews, Angela Giglio. (2004). Adapting Manipulatives To Foster The Mathematical Thinking Of Young Children. *Teaching Children Mathematics.* 11:1, 15-17.

Clements, Douglas H. and Samara, Julie. Mathematics Everywhere, Every Time. *Teaching Children Mathematics.* 10:8, 421-426.

Copley, J. V. (2000). *The Young Child and Mathematics.* Washington, DC: National Association for the Education of Young Children.

Copley, Juanita V., Glass, Kristin, Nix, Linda, Faseler, Jennifer, DeJesus, Maria, and Tanksley, Sheila. Measuring Experiences for Young Children. *Teaching Children Mathematics.* 10:6, 314-319.

Dobbs, Jennifer, Doctoroff, Greta L. and Fisher, Paige H. (2003). The "Mathis Everywhere" Preschool Mathematics Curriculum. *Teaching Children Mathematics. 10:1, 20-25.*

Esposito, L, and Ness, D. (in press) Getting Started with Numbers. In *Professional Development Handbook, Level K.* Boston: Houghton Mifflin.

National Research Council. (2001). *Adding it Up: Helping Children Learn Mathematics.* Washington, DC: National Academy Press.

National Research Council. (2000). *Eager to Learn: Educating our Preschoolers.* Washington, DC: National Academy Press.

National Council of Teachers of Mathematics. (1989). *Curriculum and Evaluation Standards for School Mathematics.* Reston, VA: NCTM.

National Council of Teachers of Mathematics. (2001) *Navigating Through Algebra in Prekindergarten - grade 2.* Reston, VA: NCTM.

National Council of Teachers of Mathematics. (2000). *Principles and Standards for School Mathematics.* Reston, VA: NCTM.

Neil, Marilyn S. 2001. Preschool in *Encyclopedia of Mathematics Education.* Louise S. Grinstein and Sally I. Lipsey, eds. P. 552- 557.

Shaw, J. M. & Blake, S. (1998). *Mathematics for Young Children.* Upper Saddle Creek, NJ: Merrill.